The Day The Rain Came

Written by: Claire White and Heather White
Illustrated by: Michael Foreman and primary school children

Dedicated to children and their families all over the world affected by flooding

for Shelter Box

michael foreman 2011

Introduction by Michael Foreman

Imagine the horror of suddenly losing your home because of a natural or man-made disaster. Gone is the place where you feel safe, where you have good food and a warm place to sleep each night.

ShelterBox invited children all over the UK to take part in a special illustration competition to visualise just such a disaster.

The Day The Rain Came shows how the children responded, with dramatic and moving results.

Everyone who took part in this competition experienced the joy of making pictures (a blank sheet of paper is a wonderful thing - full of endless possibilities) but they also used it as a way for them to reach out to the wider world of children, and to show they care, and that we all live on this same island in an ocean of Space.

The response was so great that we had a very difficult job choosing the winners and we would like to thank everyone who took part.

We all know how important it is to have shelter, somewhere you can call home. The Day The Rain Came helps us understand how ordinary people, young and old, big or small, can pull together and help each other in a disaster.

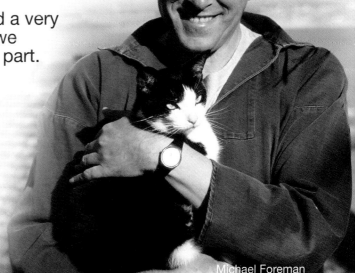

Michael Foreman

One day the **rain** came.

First came the drizzle: **spit, spot, spit, spot.**
It washed faces.

Then came the shower: **pitter, patter, pitter, patter.**
It watered plants.

Then came the rain: **splish, splash, splish, splash.**
It hammered on the roof.

Then came the downpour.

It **drummed** the earth with a deafening roar.

It rained and it rained.

It rained so hard that the stream turned into a river, the river turned into a torrent and the torrent became a **terrible** flood.

It **hurtled** down hills.

It **tore** up trees.

It **rushed** up roads.

It **carried** off cars.

It **galloped** through gardens.

It **filled** up fields.

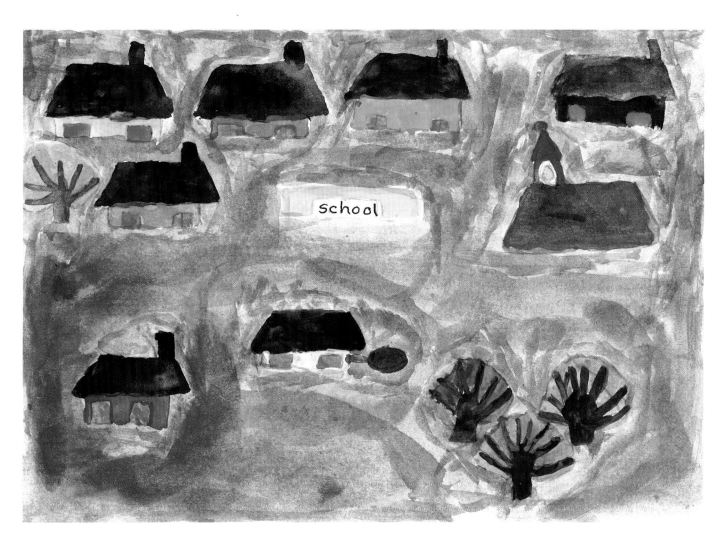

When it **stopped** raining the water did not go.

People perched on rooftops and sat in trees watching their belongings float by.

They **called** to one another sharing stories of what they had lost until it got dark.

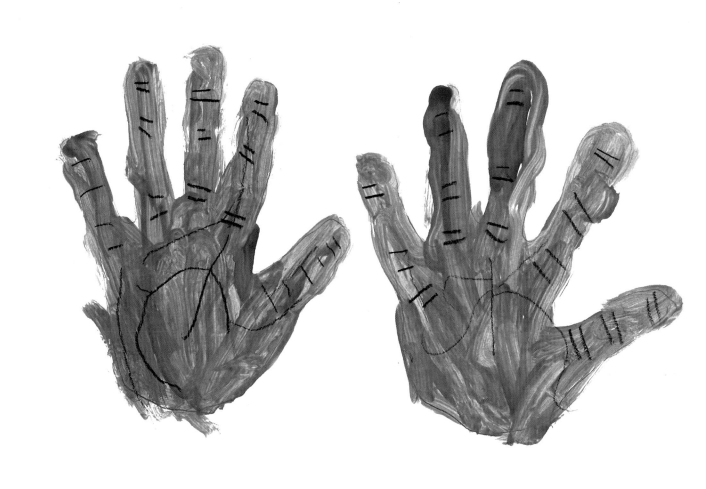

"Stop!" Shouted one. "The rain swept away our houses but we still have our hands. When the water goes we will build again and have new homes."

"The rain carried off our cars but we still have our feet. When the water goes we will **walk** to work and **skip** to school."

"The rain washed away our crops but we still know how to plant seeds. When the water goes we will **grow grain** and **bake bread**."

"We can't make the water go but we could make a **wish**."

"I **wish** for help to come," whispered one.

"I **wish** for a warm bed," whispered the next.

"I **wish** for a hot meal," said another.

Voices **filled** the air and **wishes** rang out into the night as they watched the stars together and waited for their **WISHES TO COME TRUE.**

WISHES COME TRUE

2010 was a difficult year for Rahmat and Abdurazar, mother and father of Samreen, Amna, Irfan, Sidra and Shuhbaz. They live in northern Pakistan and their lives were turned upside down when they lost their home because of a massive flood.

The flood was caused by a great landslide that blocked the Hunza River creating an ever-rising lake. Eventually that lake spilled out over the land damaging houses, roads, fields and businesses. Rahmat and Abdurazar's family lost everything. For months they joined the 40,000 others made homeless, trying to find shelter in drier areas and relying on kind people to give them food to survive.

Eventually, they were able to move back to their home village of Bash Rangoo but they still had nowhere to stay. This was an even bigger problem for Abdurazar because without their home, he needed to remain with his family to make sure they were safe. However, staying with them meant he could not go to work and earn money for basic things, like food.

Life was very hard for Abdurazar and his family but one day they discovered people in other parts of the world were sending them help. They were given a ShelterBox and although they didn't have their house back, the ShelterBox tent meant they had somewhere they could call their own. Abdurazar was then able to go to work and the family were able to start rebuilding their lives.

MAP & FACTS

PAKISTAN
HUNZA VALLEY

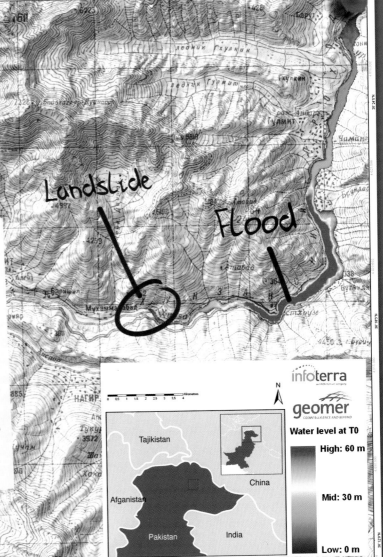

Landslide

Flood

* Around 162,420,000 people live in Pakistan.

* Most of the people who live in Pakistan live along the Indus River.

* The Indus River is the longest in Pakistan, it begins in Tibet and flows into the Arabian Sea.

* The capital of Pakistan is Islamabad.

* The currency in Pakistan is the Pakistani rupee.

* The great mountains of the Hindu Kush in Pakistan are home to the world's second highest mountain after Everest, it's name is K2 (8,611 metres high).

infoterra

geomer
GEOINTELLIGENCE AND BEYOND

Water level at T0

High: 60 m

Mid: 30 m

Low: 0 m

Tajikistan

China

Afganistan

Pakistan

India

IMAGINE

if you lost your home in a disaster...

What would you need to survive?

ShelterBox is an international disaster relief charity.

It sends big green ShelterBoxes filled with all the important things a family need to survive when they have lost their home after a disaster.

young ShelterBox

Have a look to see what's inside

EXPLORE OUR WORLD!

You can get involved and explore our world at **www.youngshelterbox.org**
Tell your teacher about our special teachers' area there too.
It's full of fantastic pictures, film footage and lots more.

WHAT'S IN A BOX?

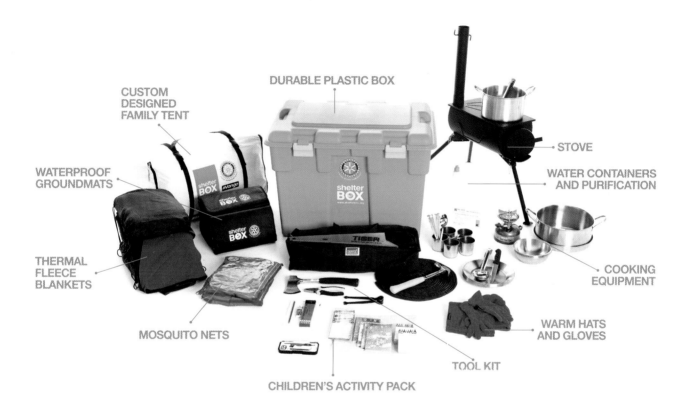

CUSTOM DESIGNED FAMILY TENT

DURABLE PLASTIC BOX

WATERPROOF GROUNDMATS

STOVE

WATER CONTAINERS AND PURIFICATION

THERMAL FLEECE BLANKETS

COOKING EQUIPMENT

MOSQUITO NETS

WARM HATS AND GLOVES

TOOL KIT

CHILDREN'S ACTIVITY PACK

Buying this book means you've helped us carry on sending these important things to families when they need them the most.

Illustration Credits

Page 1: **Rebecca Whitbread**, Mithian School, Cornwall

Page 4: **Gabriella Graham**, Stanley Infant & Junior School, Falkland Islands

Page 5: **Tilly Fry**, Headington Prep School, Oxfordshire

Page 6: **Olivia Cooke**, The Bishops' CEVA Primary School, Cornwall

Page 7: **Spencer English**, Duloe CEVA Junior & Infant School, Cornwall

Page 8: **Darcy Pascoe**, Constantine Primary School, Cornwall

Page 9: **Kensi Hoskin**, Treverbyn Academy, Cornwall

Page 10: **Oliver Fay**, Yealmpton Primary School, Devon

Page 11: **Ella Wallis**, Constantine Primary School, Cornwall

Page 12: **Luke Simmons**, Keresforth Primary School, Yorkshire

Page 13: **Hannah Carroll**, Yealmpton Primary School, Devon

Page 14: **Guste Klimasauskaite**, West Twyford Primary School, London

Page 15: **Kyana Smith**, Headington Prep School, Oxfordshire

Page 16: **Aoife Soni** Headington Prep School, Oxfordshire

Page 17: **Tia Saunderson**, Yealmpton Primary School, Devon

Page 19: **Ben van Veen**, Constantine Primary School, Cornwall

Page 20: **Polly Wilson**, Headington Prep School, Oxfordshire

Back Page: **Tara Nahidi**, West Twyford Primary School, London